25 MODERN PIANO SOLOS
THE VELVET TOUCH

M786:2

Cover Design   Malcolm Rasala
(photo)   Andy Lane

First Published 1984
© International Music Publications

Exclusive Distributors
International Music Publications
60/70 Roden Street, Ilford, England

215-2-169

BAKER STREET

Words and Music by GERRY RAFFERTY

BEGIN THE BEGUINE

Words and Music
by COLE PORTER

8

BODY AND SOUL

Words by ROBERT SOUR,
EDWARD HEYMAN and FRANK EYTON
Music by JOHN GREEN

BORN FREE

Words by DON BLACK
Music by JOHN BARRY

CAVATINA

Music by STANLEY MYERS

20

DO YOU KNOW WHERE YOU'RE GOING TO?

(Theme from Mahogany)

3RD APRIL 1976
Nº 5   8 WKS
DIANA ROSS

Words by GERRY GOFFIN
Music by MIKE MASSER

24

25

EMBRACEABLE YOU

1930

FROM THE MUSICAL 'CRAZY GIRL'

Words by IRA GERSHWIN
Music by GEORGE GERSHWIN

FEELINGS (¿DIME?)

27TH SEP 1975
Nº 4   10 WKS
MORRIS ALBERT'S ONLY HIT
BRAZILIAN VOCALIST

English Words and Music by MORRIS ALBERT
Spanish Lyrics by THOMAS FUNDORA

IF

22ND FEB 1975
No 1   9 WKS
TELLY SAVALAS

Words and Music
by DAVID GATES

THE LIFE AND TIMES OF DAVID LLOYD GEORGE *(Chi Mai)*

Music by ENNIO MORRICONE

I LEFT MY HEART IN SAN FRANCISCO

27 MAY 30 SEP 9 DEC 1965
N° 25 7 WKS
TONY BENNETT

Words by DOUGLASS CROSS
Music by GEORGE CORY

42

43

IT'S MY TURN

17TH JAN 1981
Nº 16   8 WKS
DIANA ROSS

Words by CAROLE BAYER SAGER
Music by MICHAEL MASSER

THE LAST TIME I SAW PARIS

1940

FROM THE FILM
'LADY BE GOOD'

Words by OSCAR HAMMERSTEIN II
Music by JEROME KERN

2 *MY FOOLISH HEART*

1949

Words by NED WASHINGTON
Music by VICTOR YOUNG

54

SLEEPY SHORES

18 DEC 1971
Nº 8   15 WKS
JOHNNY PEARSON

Music by JOHNNY PEARSON

SPREAD A LITTLE HAPPINESS

1928

Words by CLIFFORD GREY
Music by VIVIAN ELLIS

59

STAY AS SWEET AS YOU ARE

1934

Words and Music by
MACK GORDON and **HARRY REVEL**

64

STRANGER ON THE SHORE

30 NOV 1961   14 JUN 1962
N° 2   55 WKS   N° 30   10 WKS
ACKER BILK   ANDY WILLIAMS

Words by ROBERT MELLIN
Muisc by ACKER BILK

68

70 3 THEY DIDN'T BELIEVE ME 1914

FROM THE MUSICAL
'THE GIRL FROM UTAH'
WORDS BY HERBERT REYNOLDS ?

Words by M E ROURKE
Music by JEROME D KERN

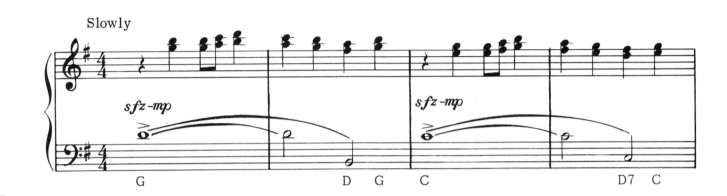

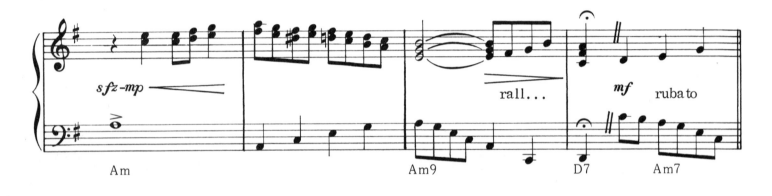

TONIGHT, I CELEBRATE MY LOVE

20TH AUG 1983
N°2   13 WKS
PEABO BRYSON
ROBERTA FLACK

Words and Music by
MICHAEL MASSER and GERRY GOFFIN

76

UP WHERE WE BELONG

15 JAN 1983
Nº 7 13 WKS
JOE COCKER
JENNIFER WARNES

Words by WILL JENNINGS
Music by BUFFY SAINTE-MARIE
and JACK NITZSCHE

THE VERY THOUGHT OF YOU

1934

Words and Music
by RAY NOBLE

84

CRY ME A RIVER

1953

5 APR 1957   *19 MAR 1983*
Nº 22   3 WKS   *Nº 27   7 WKS*
JULIE LONDON   *MARI WILSON*

Words and Music
by ARTHUR HAMILTON

88

90

THE WAY WE WERE

30 MAR. 1974   5 APR 1975
Nº 31   6 WKS   Nº 4   15 WKS
BARBRA STREISAND   GLADYS KNIGHT
                      AND THE PIPS

Words by ALAN and MARILYN BERGMAN
Music by MARVIN HAMLISCH

92

LOVE THEME FROM "THE WINDS OF WAR"

Music by BOB COBERT

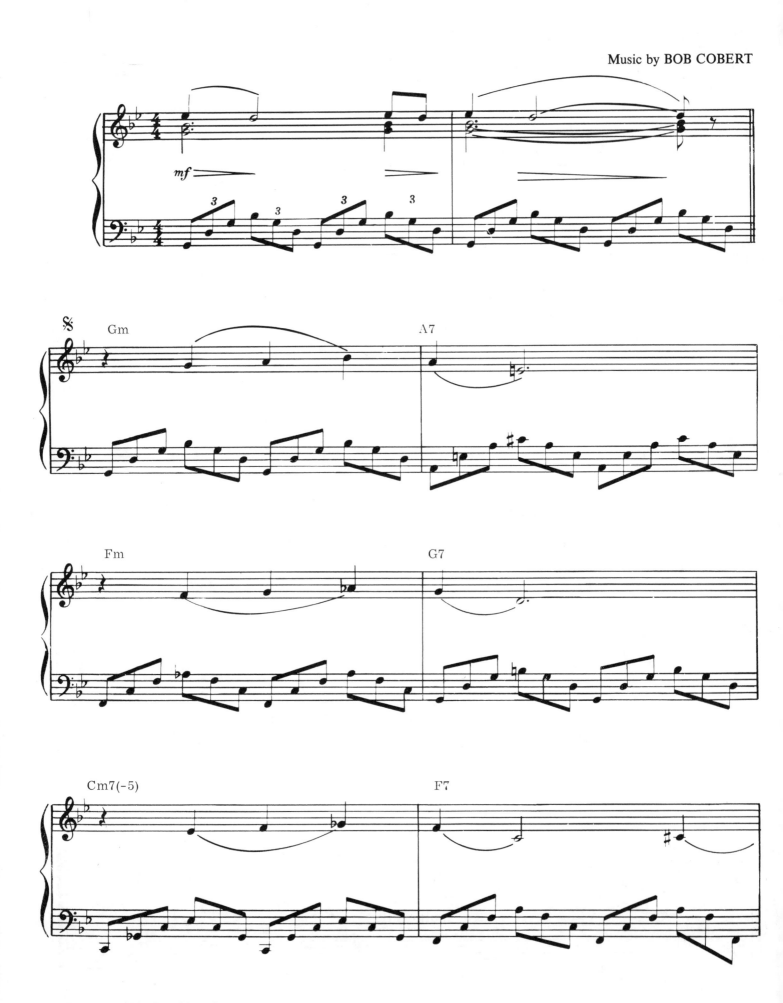

Printed by Halstan & Co. Ltd., Amersham, Bucks., England